HELP WITH HOMEWORK
ENGLISH
ESSENTIALS

years

HI, MY NAME IS KITCAT...

... AND I'M DIG.

WE ARE HERE TO HELP YOU THROUGH THESE EXERCISES. START AT THE BEGINNING AND DON'T DO TOO MUCH IN ONE GO.

IT WON'T BE EASY ALL THE TIME. SOME PAGES CAN BE TRICKY, BUT WE'VE GIVEN YOU THE ANSWERS AT THE BACK IN CASE YOU GET REALLY STUCK. NO PEEPING, THOUGH! YOU WILL RECOGNISE A LOT OF THIS FROM THE WORK YOU DO AT SCHOOL. NOW DON'T YOU WISH YOU'D PAID MORE ATTENTION?! GOOD LUCK!

Autumn
Publishing

Know your nouns

A **noun** is a person, place or thing.

The sentences below don't make sense because the nouns are incorrect. Cross out the noun (underlined) and replace it with a noun from the box.

1. I hurt my __hair__. _____

2. The __river__ is still wet. _____

3. Don't touch the __clouds__! _____

4. Red is my favourite __dish__. _____

5. Can I have a __lion__? _____

6. Let's go for a __sky__. _____

Nouns:

walk	exhibits	paint
colour	biscuit	knee

Get it?

The word 'walk' can be a noun or a verb depending on how it is used in the sentence. E.g. 'a walk' is a noun but 'he walks' is a verb. If you can write 'a' or 'an' before the word, it is usually a noun.

Noun phrases include a noun, plus any other words that modify (describe) the noun. You can also use preposition phrases to describe a noun.

Use the determiners and preposition phrases to complete the sentences below.

Determiners:

her	those
some	three
the	that

Preposition phrases:

around the corner	from the book
in the garden	over there
on platform 5	in the basket

1. Look at _____ beautiful cherry tree _____ .

2. She dressed up as _____ favourite character _____ .

3. I like _____ puppies _____ .

4. The pencil case belongs to Ben. It's _____ .

5. Catch _____ next train _____ .

Expanded noun phrases

Preposition phrases can tell you more about a noun, such as where it is or when it is.

For example: **the old, stone wall at the end of the garden**.

The words 'old' and 'stone' are adjectives describing the wall. The phrase 'at the end of the garden' is a prepositional phrase telling you where the wall is.

To complete the table below, fill in the blank spaces by choosing adjectives, nouns and preposition phrases to make expanded noun phrases.

Adjectives:	Noun:	Preposition phrase:
the warm, bright	sun	in the morning
	clown	with a red nose
a ferocious	dog	
those terrifying, dark		at midnight
		over the hills

Create some of your own in the table below.

Adjectives:	Noun:	Preposition phrase:

Adding adjectives

An **adjective** is a describing word that tells you more about a noun.

For example, a building… a **new** building… a **wonderful, new** building

Underline the adjectives in the sentences below.

1. The clever detective caught the notorious thief.

2. Spectacular fireworks lit up the night sky.

3. A gigantic, hairy spider sat beside the nervous boy.

Get it?

Adding adjectives before nouns will make your writing more interesting and informative for the reader.

Select the most appropriate adjectives from the box on the right to describe each noun in these sentences. Then write the new sentences on the lines below.

Adjectives:

comfortable	excitable
terrified	flowing
delicious	Japanese

1. The dog chased the cat.

_____

2. We had a meal in a restaurant.

_____

3. She wore a dress and shoes.

_____

Stick a reward sticker here!

4

Perfect your pronouns

Pronouns are useful because they can be used instead of repeating a noun. Pronouns can also be used to link sentences.

Replace the nouns (underlined below) with personal pronouns from the box.

1. The reds beat the blues. <u>The reds</u> won by two points. _____

2. Jack loved the film when <u>Jack</u> saw <u>the film</u>. _____

3. Bella is in my class. Do you know <u>Bella</u>? _____

4. Our neighbours are friendly when you get to know <u>our neighbours</u>. _____

Personal pronouns:	
I	you
we / us	it
him / her	he / she
they / them	

Possessive pronouns tell you who owns something, e.g. The bike belongs to Tom. It's **his**.

Choose a possessive pronoun to complete each of the following sentences:

1. The ice cream belongs to Amy. It's _____ .

2. The snake belongs to us. It's _____ .

3. The hat belongs to you. It's _____ .

4. The car belongs to them. It's _____ .

Possessive pronouns:	
ours	yours
mine	theirs
his	its
hers	

5. The pencil case belongs to Ben. It's _____ .

6. The dog belongs to us. It's _____ .

7. The book belongs to you. It's _____ .

8. The ball belongs to me. It's _____ .

Stick a reward sticker here!

5

Verbs and adverbs

A **verb** is a doing word. It tells us about the action taking place.

Which of these sentences sounds the most interesting?

WEAK VERB

1. The boy **went** across the field.

BETTER VERB

2. The boy **ran** across the field.

VERB + ADVERB

3. The boy **ran quickly** across the field*.

STRONG VERB

4. The boy **sprinted** across the field.

Get it?

The sentence with the strong verb is the most interesting. It gives the reader a clear picture of the action. One strong word is better than lots of weak words.

*If the verb is not very strong, then an adverb is needed, e.g. **ran quickly**. You wouldn't need to add **quickly** after **sprinted** because **sprinted** is strong enough to convey the action.

Choose the most appropriate strong verbs to complete the sentences below.

1. The racecar **dawdled / trundled / screeched** around the track.

2. The mouse **meandered / strolled / scampered** under the sofa.

3. The waves **crashed / trickled / dribbled** onto the rocks.

4. The girl **hollered / whispered / shouted** the secret to her friend.

5. The boy **stomped / clattered / crept** through the spooky house.

An **adverb** tells us more about a verb. It tells us **how**, **when** or **where** the action of the verb takes place, e.g. the boy ran **quickly**.

Write an adverb after these verbs. Choose from the box or use your own.

1. He looked _____ at his opponent.

2. They spoke _____ on the phone.

3. She sang _____ into the microphone.

4. The wind blew _____ .

5. The volcano erupted _____ .

Adverbs:

fiercely	quietly
angrily	jokingly
outside	still
kindly	loudly
suddenly	gently

Some adverbs are used to show how possible or certain things can be.

For example:

You **definitely** should do your homework before athletics.

Here are some examples of adverbs for possibility: possibly, surely, perhaps, mostly, definitely.

Adverbs for possibility:

possibly

surely

perhaps

mostly

definitely

Choose the most appropriate adverbs for the sentences below:

1. It could _____ snow tomorrow.

2. _____ you could come swimming with me on Saturday.

3. It _____ will get dark tonight.

Get it?
An adverb can change the meaning of the verb. For example, someone can look **suspiciously** or move **curiously** around a room.

Stick a reward sticker here!

Adverbial phrases

Adverbial phrases modify a verb. They do the same job as an adverb but are a group of words. An adverbial phrase gives us more information about the time, place and manner of the action being described.

For example:

How - the boy ran **with haste**

When - the sun set **after tea**

Where - the children played **behind the wall**

Here is a newspaper report about a burglar who broke into a jewellery shop. Underline the adverbial phrases in this newspaper report:

Yesterday, at 11:58pm, a burglar broke into a jewellery shop on John Street.

It is claimed that the criminal threw a large rock through the front window and robbed the shop within minutes.

The jeweller, who lived above the shop, awoke to the sound of the shop alarm going off below his flat. By the time he ran downstairs, the burglar had escaped down the street, carrying a large bag of expensive digital watches.

The suspect has not yet been found.

ADVERBIAL PHRASES TELL US HOW, WHEN AND WHERE AN ACTION TOOK PLACE.

Playing with words

Similes are when you describe something as being <u>like</u> something else.

For example, the rocks were jagged **like shark's teeth**.

Make up some of your own similes to complete these descriptions:

1. The crashing waves were like _____

2. The hot sun was like _____

3. The autumn leaves were like _____

4. The tiger's eyes were like _____

Metaphors are when you say that something <u>is</u> something else.

For example, She's a clown! (She is always joking.)

Choose a metaphor from the box on the right to describe these people or things.

Metaphors:

A snake in the grass   A ray of sunshine

A fly in the ointment   A night owl

1. Someone who is always smiling. _____

2. Someone who is sneaky. _____

3. Someone who stays up late. _____

Onomatopoeia is a word that sounds like the thing it is describing.

BUZZ!   CRASH!   POP!   GLUG!   SQUELCH!   PLOP!   SQUEAK!

Write some more examples of onomatopoeia:

_____

_____

Full stops and capitals

We put a **full stop** (.) at the end of a main clause. New sentences always start with a capital letter.

Read the following passage and add full stops in the right place.

i wake up each morning before the alarm i wait for it to ring on the dot of seven and then i get up however today was going to be different i didn't wake up the alarm didn't ring this difference would change my life forever

Go back to the same passage above and add capital letters for 'I', and for the start of each sentence.

Now check against the following text:

I wake up each morning before the alarm. I wait for it to ring on the dot of seven and then I get up. However today was going to be different. I didn't wake up. The alarm didn't ring. This difference would change my life forever.

How did you score? Give yourself one point for each correct full stop and capital letter.

Stick a reward sticker here!

My score: _____

Semicolons and colons

Stick a reward sticker here!

A **semicolon** (;) joins parts of a sentence where there are closely connected ideas.

For example:

I didn't wake up; the alarm didn't ring.

Write a sentence that contains a semicolon. Use it to link your ideas together.

_____

Colons (:) appear at the start of a list or just before an explanation.

For example:

To make my favourite sandwich, you will need: bread, margarine, tuna and cucumber. Here's why I like it so much: it's delicious.

If you are writing a complicated list, you can use semicolons to help you separate the items.

For example:

To make my favourite sandwich, you will need: wholemeal or brown bread, cut into two slices; thinly-sliced cucumber; drained tuna flakes; and reduced-fat, low-salt margarine.

Write a list of ingredients (starting with a colon) for your favourite sandwich. Add commas and/or semicolons to separate items in the list.

For my favourite sandwich, you will need

_____

How to use apostrophes

Apostrophes have two important jobs:

1. An apostrophe tells you who owns what – this is called **possession**. For example, the shark's teeth (the teeth belonging to the shark).

2. An apostrophe tells you which words are shortened – this is called **contraction**. For example, It's a shark! (It is a shark!)

Write a phrase containing a possessive apostrophe for each of the statements below.

The first one has been done for you.

1. the desk belonging to the teacher ___the teacher's desk___

2. the purse belonging to Mum _____

3. the studio belonging to the artist _____

4. the whiskers belonging to the cat _____

If the noun is a plural ending in 's', the apostrophe goes at the end.

Write a phrase containing a plural possessive apostrophe for the statements below.

The first one has been done for you.

1. the dog belonging to the girls ___the girls' dog___

2. the car belonging to the family _____

3. the changing room belonging to the players _____

4. the jobs belonging to the people _____

5. the toys belonging to the babies _____

12

Apostrophes are also used when you want to shorten words or phrases. The apostrophe replaces the missing letters.

> HELP! I CAN'T SWIM!

Learn these contractions:

I am – **I'm**
he is / she is – **he's** / **she's**
it is – **it's**
you are – **you're**
they are – **they're**
we are – **we're**

do not – **don't**
did not – **didn't**
does not – **doesn't**
cannot – **can't**
could not – **couldn't**
would not – **wouldn't**

Use an apostrophe to shorten words in each of the sentences below.

The first one has been done for you.

1. We cannot go yet.   We can't go yet.

2. She would have liked the taste.

3. The dog does not bite.

4. The car should have started.

5. It is not fair!

> HOW DO YOU STOP A DOG FROM SMELLING?

> HOLD ITS NOSE! (NOT: IT'S NOSE!)

Speech
(inverted commas for direct speech)

Stick a reward sticker here!

Inverted commas (" ") tell you exactly what words are spoken by the characters in a story.

Get it?

Inverted commas are drawn at the beginning and at the end of direct speech. All other punctuation (including full stops) goes inside them.

Read the story extract and draw inverted commas around the words that are said by the characters.

I think Dig is sick, said Tom. He won't eat his dinner.

Perhaps he's not hungry, replied Tom's mum.

But he's *always* hungry! said Tom. And it's his favourite: marinated chicken chunks in juicy jelly.

Continue the conversation between Tom and his mum on the lines below. Start a new line for each new speaker. Draw inverted commas around the words that are spoken.

HE'S JUST ATTENTION-SEEKING!

Conversation often has question marks or exclamation marks.

Question marks (?) tell you that a question is being asked.

Exclamation marks (!) show surprise, humour or excitement.

Read the story extract below. Change the punctuation by substituting question marks or exclamation marks where you think they belong.

"Mum," shouted Tom.

"Now what," said Tom's mum.

"I know why Dig won't eat his dinner," said Tom. "It's a new recipe. They've added vegetables. You know he hates vegetables."

Continue the conversation between Tom and his mum on the lines below. Include inverted commas, question marks and exclamation marks where necessary.

AW, DIDDUMS WON'T EAT HIS VEGETABLES!

Clauses and conjunctions

Stick a reward sticker here!

A sentence or a clause has to include a noun and a verb.

For example:
Dig loves chicken.

Dig is a noun and **loves** is a verb.

A **conjunction** is a connecting word that links clauses or sentences.

For example:
Dig loves chicken. He hates vegetables.
Dig loves chicken **but** he hates vegetables.

Use a conjunction to join these sentences together.

Coordinating conjunctions	Subordinating conjunctions
and	when
but	because
or	if
yet	that
so	while
	although

1. Dig didn't eat his dinner. Kit ate it instead.

_____

2. Dig and Kit were friends. They were rivals, too.

_____

3. Tom was worried. Dig hadn't eaten his food.

_____

4. Mum wasn't paying attention. She was busy.

_____

Write a sentence of your own using a conjunction.

_____

Underline the conjunctions in these sentences.

1. I put the dog on the lead and we went out for a walk.

2. It felt cold although it was sunny.

3. We played in the park until it was dark.

4. Mum was cross when I got home late.

5. I missed my programme because it came on earlier than usual.

Write another sentence of your own using a conjunction.

_____

Sometimes we use **connecting adverbs** to link sentences and paragraphs so that our writing 'flows' better.

For example:
We were watching TV. Suddenly, all the lights went out.

Underline the adverbs that connect these sentences.

1. I missed the last five minutes of the film. Consequently, I don't know how it ended!

2. I can come to your house. However, I can't stay for long.

3. Firstly, you mix the butter and the sugar. Next, you add the egg.

4. Dad did the shopping. Meanwhile, Mum was at work.

5. Do your homework now. Later, you can go swimming.

Some connecting adverbs:

later

suddenly

finally

firstly

next

additionally

meanwhile

consequently

Write two sentences of your own and connect them using a connecting adverb.

_____

_____

_____

_____

Get it?

However is a connecting adverb.

Relative clauses

Relative clauses are a type of clause added into a sentence to give more detail about the nouns. They work a bit like adjectives.

Relative clauses begin with a relative pronoun: **who**, **when**, **where**, **which**, **that** or **whose**.

When a relative clause is in the middle of a sentence, commas are used around the clause to mark it.

For example:

The boy, **who walked along the wall**, was good at balancing.

The house, **where my Nan lived**, was the largest on the street.

Sometimes, relative clauses can come at the end of a sentence. When they are at the end of a sentence, a comma is not used.

E.g. I love the food that Dad cooks.

Add a relative clause to the following sentences. Don't forget to add commas!

The friends _____ decided to meet at the park.

Cheetahs _____ can run extremely fast.

The town _____ _____ was difficult to find.

The necklace _____ _____ _____ was very precious.

Parenthesis
(using brackets, dashes and commas)

Stick a reward sticker here!

You can use other types of punctuation to mark extra information or relative clauses. As well as commas, you can use brackets and dashes to add extra information.

Commas work best with relative clauses:

The bus driver, **who was aged 46,** travelled down the wrong side of the road.

Brackets are useful when you give a short, succinct version of the information:

The bus driver **(aged 46)** travelled down the wrong side of the road.

Dashes are good for informal comments. They are used in texts like emails and diaries:

The bus driver – **unbelievably** – travelled down the wrong side of the road.

Work out which punctuation works best in the following sentences. Add **brackets**, **dashes** or **commas** into the boxes in the sentences below.

The staircase ☐ 735 steps ☐ winds around the inside of the castle.

The Himalayas ☐ where the largest mountain in the world is situated ☐ are in Nepal.

The weather ☐ thunder and lightning ☐ spoiled our barbecue.

The car ☐ annoyingly ☐ would not start when we needed to get to school.

Prefix

A **prefix** is a group of letters added to the beginning of a word that changes the word's meaning.

For example:
preschool
prehistoric

The prefix 'pre' means 'before' (in Latin).

Add prefixes to these words.

1. 'aqua' (means 'water' in Latin)

    _ _ _ _ rium

    _ _ _ _ _ tic

    _ _ _ _ marine

2. 'viv' (means 'live' in Latin)

    _ _ _ isect

    _ _ _ acious

    _ _ id

3. 'geo' (means 'Earth' in Greek)

    _ _ _ metry

    _ _ _ logy

    _ _ _ graphy

4. 'bio' (means 'life' in Greek)

    _ _ _ graphy

    _ _ _ nic

    _ _ _ logical

5. 'oct' (means 'eight' in Greek)

    _ _ _ opus

    _ _ _ agon

    _ _ _ ave

6. 'super' (means 'over' or 'above' in Latin)

    _ _ _ _ _ market

    _ _ _ _ _ sonic

    _ _ _ _ _ _ visor

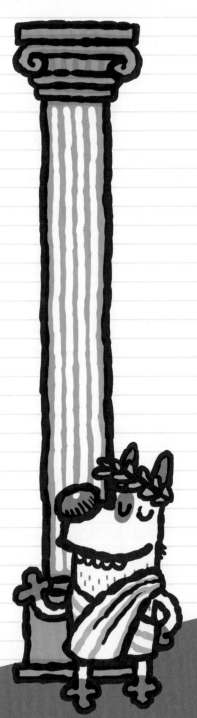

Suffix

A **suffix** is a group of letters added to the end of a word.

Using a suffix can change the tense (from past to present tense and vice versa) or the meaning of a word.

Suffixes:

-en / -ed	-ish	-ation	-less	-ment
-er / -or	-ing	-ful	-ly	-ness

Add suffixes to these words.

1. instruct + or = _____

2. act + or = _____

3. conduct + or = _____

4. hope + less = _____

5. sleep + less = _____

6. rest + less = _____

7. excite + ment = _____

8. move + ment = _____

9. agree + ment = _____

10. immediate + ly = _____

11. sudden + ly = _____

12. extreme + ly = _____

When the root word ends in a vowel and you want to add a suffix that starts with a vowel, you drop one of the vowels.

Try these:

1. spice + ed = _____

2. care + ing = _____

3. late + er = _____

Double the consonant when there is a single vowel before a single consonant, e.g. sit + ing = sitting.

Try these:

4. big + est = _____

5. swim + ing = _____

6. stop + ed = _____

Learn these:
beauty + ful = beautiful
happy + ness = happiness

Get it?

The vowels are: **a, e, i, o, u.** The other letters in the alphabet are called consonants.

Stick a reward sticker here!

21

Different kinds of writing

Diaries, letters and autobiographies are written in the **first person** using the pronouns **I**, **my**, **mine** and **we**.

Underline the first-person pronouns in this diary extract:

Somehow I knew that today was going to be special, even though it started off like every other day – I was going to be late for school again!

Instructions and advertisements are written in the **second person** using the pronouns **you** and **your**.

Underline the second-person pronouns in this instruction text:

To make chocolate brownies you need: flour, cocoa powder, eggs, butter and milk. But first, you need to find an adult to help you!

Novels, stories, information books and newspaper reports are often written in the **third person** using the pronouns **he**, **she**, **it** and **they**.

Underline the third-person pronouns in this story extract:

"I'm so happy!" she said. "I want to thank everyone who voted for me!" They cheered enthusiastically as she lifted the winner's trophy.

Write three pieces of text – one in the first person, one in the second person and one in the third person.

LOOK FOR EXAMPLES IN BOOKS TO HELP YOU.

First person

_____

_____

_____

_____

Second person

_____

_____

_____

_____

Third person

_____

_____

_____

_____

Get it?

There are two main types of writing. **Fiction** is not true; it is made up by the storyteller. **Non-fiction** is true; it is writing based on facts and real events.

23

Writing stories (fiction)

> When you write a story the first thing you need to decide on is where and when the action takes place – this is called the **setting**.

Writers often set their stories in places that are familiar to them, for example school, home, neighbourhood, workplace or somewhere they went on holiday.

Possible settings:

new school	raging river	remote rainforest
busy airport	noisy campsite	space station

Choose one of these settings and write notes on the mind map below about the things you can see, hear, touch, taste or smell.

> USE A SEPARATE PIECE OF PAPER IF YOU NEED MORE SPACE TO WRITE.

> DECIDE WHETHER THE SETTING IS IN THE PAST, PRESENT OR FUTURE.

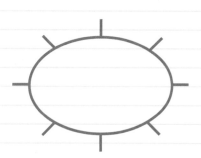

Characters are essential to tell the story.

Any characters you invent should have a clear purpose in the story and a distinct personality. They might be unusual in some way, e.g. in the way they dress or speak.

Match the following characters to the settings in the box above.
There are no right or wrong answers.

Polly Phonic – friendly, talkative	**Venus Strange** – clever, mysterious
Miss McEvil – controlling, ambitious	**Gazza Green** – loud, outdoorsy-type
Ace Bravado – daredevil, adventure seeker	**Leif Biome** – wacky, curious nature

Now choose one of these characters and invent others to match your chosen setting. Make up names and character descriptions. Use a separate piece of paper for this work.

All stories must have a **plot** or **theme** – this is what the story is about and what the characters do.

Here are some popular story ideas:

Possible plots:

| good versus evil | a misunderstanding | a comedy |
| something is lost or stolen | journey of discovery | friendship theme |

Choose a plot to match your setting and characters.

Write a story plan in five paragraphs:

Beginning – introduce your setting and characters

_____

_____

Build up – things start to happen and the plot develops

_____

_____

Crisis – a series of things go wrong, leading to a crisis

_____

_____

Solution – the characters manage to sort out the problem

_____

_____

Ending – the characters reflect on what has happened or changed

_____

_____

Now you are ready to write out your story in full!
Use a separate piece of paper for this.

Stick a reward sticker here!

Writing non-fiction

Reports, recounts, instructions and discussions are examples of **non-fiction** writing.

Reports – writing about the facts known on a given topic. Use specialist vocabulary and define the terms used. Use a formal style in present tense. Illustrate with diagrams or pictures.

Recounts – writing about an event you have witnessed or an experience you have had. Use pronouns: I, we, he, she, they. Write in the past tense using powerful verbs. Use time connectives such as: then, when, later, next, eventually.

Instructions – writing about how to do something. Include lists of materials needed. Write a clear sequence of steps. Use verbs. For example: cut, mix, stir, place. Use time connectives and pronouns such as you and your.

Discussions – writing about a topic to provide a balanced viewpoint or discussion. Write the points 'for' and 'against', using evidence to back up the argument. Use present tense and emotional language to engage with the reader. Reach a conclusion at the end.

Read the following report text:

Fast Cats

The cheetah is the fastest land animal. Cheetahs can reach speeds of up to 70 miles per hour (113 kph). They can accelerate faster than the average car: 0-60 miles per hour (0-97 kph) in only 3 seconds!

Their long legs and athletic bodies are built for fast acceleration. Wildebeest, their prey, are fast, too, but they are slower to accelerate. The cheetah, however, can't maintain this speed over long distances so sometimes the wildebeest manage to outrun them.

Larger cats such as leopards and tigers are slower because their bulkier bodies have to use more muscle and energy to propel them forwards. They can reach up to 35-40 miles per hour (56-65 kph) in short bursts.

Domestic cats can run up to 30 miles per hour (48 kph). They have lost some of their speed because they no longer need to chase their dinner!

Now answer these questions in complete sentences:

1. What makes the cheetah so fast?

_____

_____

2. Is the cheetah faster than the average car?

_____

_____

3. How does the wildebeest manage to outrun the cheetah?

_____

_____

4. Why have domestic cats lost some of their speed?

_____

_____

5. What tense (past, present or future) is the text written in?

_____

_____

Stick a reward sticker here!

A discussion

Read the following discussion text:

Do dogs make good pets?

People have kept dogs as pets for hundreds of years. Dogs can be easily house-trained to live in our homes. They form loyal and protective bonds with their owners and for older people who live alone, a dog can provide companionship. Studies have shown that dog owners tend to be happier and healthier because the daily walks they give their dogs have health benefits for them also.

However, owning a dog comes with responsibilities. Dogs need feeding, exercising, love and affection and someone to look after them when their owners go on holiday. One of the biggest complaints against dog ownership is dog-fouling. Despite fines of up to £1,000 there are still some irresponsible owners who do not clean up after their pets.

Dogs make good pets and they bring great rewards for many people, but they bring responsibilities too which should not be forgotten. Dogs are not like toys given at Christmas that can be thrown away when we tire of them – a dog is for life.

Get it?

The first paragraph outlines arguments 'for'. The second paragraph outlines arguments 'against'. The final paragraph gives a conclusion.

Write a similar balanced argument: Do cats make good pets?* Use a separate piece of paper for this.

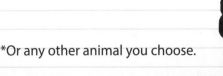

Stick a reward sticker here!

*Or any other animal you choose.

A recount

Read the following recount:

When I arrived home at 7pm, I immediately knew something was wrong. The first thing I noticed was the light through the upstairs window which I knew I hadn't left on. Then I saw that the front door was wide open! I stepped nervously into the hallway and everything looked OK. Next, I went into the living room and to my dismay I saw that some burglars had broken in! Then I called the police.

Now answer these questions in complete sentences:

1. What time connectives have been used in the text? List them below.

_____

2. What tense (past, present or future) is the text written in? Examine the verbs to find out.

_____

3. Is the text written in the first, second or third person? Explain your answer.

_____

Write a recount of a past event or experience that you can remember.
Use extra paper if needed.

_____

_____

_____

_____

_____

_____

Writing formal letters

WRITE YOUR ADDRESS HERE

THE RECIPIENT'S ADDRESS IS WRITTEN HERE

_____

_____

_____

The Manager
Pizza Palace
Garlic Street
Doughton
ET7 UP1

WRITE THE DATE HERE

WRITE A FORMAL LETTER TO COMPLAIN ABOUT THE LACK OF TOPPINGS ON A PIZZA YOU BOUGHT FROM A FAST FOOD RESTAURANT. MAKE IT CLEAR WHY YOU ARE WRITING THIS LETTER. FOR EXAMPLE, DO YOU WANT A REFUND?

_____

Dear Sir/Madam,

_____

_____

_____

_____

_____

Yours faithfully,

_____

WRITE YOUR SIGNATURE HERE

Get it?

If you know the name of the person you are addressing, you end with 'Yours sincerely'.

30

Answers

p. 2 Know your nouns
1. I hurt my knee.
2. The paint is still wet.
3. Don't touch the exhibits!
4. Red is my favourite colour.
5. Can I have a biscuit?
6. Let's go for a walk.

There are several possible answers for this activity but your answers could include:
1. Look at <u>that</u> beautiful cherry tree <u>in the garden</u>.
2. She dressed up as <u>her</u> favourite character <u>from the book</u>.
3. I like <u>those</u> puppies <u>in the basket</u>.
4. The pencil case belongs to Ben. It's <u>over there</u>.
5. Catch <u>the</u> next train <u>on platform 5</u>.

p. 4 Adding adjectives
1. The <u>clever</u> detective caught the <u>notorious</u> thief.
2. <u>Spectacular</u> fireworks lit up the <u>night</u> sky.
3. A <u>gigantic, hairy</u> spider sat beside the <u>nervous</u> boy.

1. The excitable dog chased the terrified cat.
2. We had a delicious meal in a Japanese restaurant.
3. She wore a flowing dress and comfortable shoes.

p. 5 Perfect your pronouns
1. The reds beat the blues. They won by two points.
2. Jack loved the film when he saw it.
3. Bella is in my class. Do you know her?
4. Our neighbours are friendly when you get to know them.

1. The ice cream belongs to Amy. It's hers.
2. The snake belongs to us. It's ours.
3. The hat belongs to you. It's yours.
4. The car belongs to them. It's theirs.
5. The pencil case belongs to Ben. It's his.
6. The dog belongs to us. It's ours.
7. The book belongs to you. It's yours.
8. The ball belongs to me. It's mine.

p. 6-7 Verbs and adverbs
1. The racecar **screeched** around the track.
2. The mouse **scampered** under the sofa.
3. The waves **crashed** onto the rocks.
4. The girl **whispered** the secret to her friend.
5. The boy **crept** through the spooky house.

Here are some possible answers:
1. He looked fiercely at his opponent.
2. They spoke quietly on the phone.
3. She sang softly into the microphone.
4. The wind blew gently.
5. The volcano erupted violently.

p. 8 Adverbial phrases
Yesterday, <u>at 11:58pm</u>, a burglar broke <u>into a jewellery shop on John Street</u>.
It is claimed that the criminal threw a large rock <u>through the front window</u> and robbed the shop <u>within minutes</u>.

The jeweller, who lived <u>above the shop</u>, awoke <u>to the sound of the shop alarm</u> going off <u>below his flat</u>. <u>By the time</u> he ran <u>downstairs</u>, the burglar had escaped <u>down the street</u>, carrying a large bag of expensive digital watches.

The suspect has not yet been found.

p. 9 Playing with words
1. Someone who is always smiling = A ray of sunshine
2. Someone who is sneaky = A snake in the grass
3. Someone who stays up late = A night owl

p. 12-13 How to use apostrophes
1. the teacher's desk
2. Mum's purse
3. the artist's studio
4. the cat's whiskers

1. the girls' dog
2. the family's car
3. the players' changing room
4. the people's jobs
5. the babies' toys

1. We can't go yet.
2. She would've liked the taste.
3. The dog doesn't bite.
4. The car should've started.
5. It's not fair! / It isn't fair!

p. 14-15 Speech

"I think Dig is sick," said Tom. "He won't eat his dinner."
"Perhaps he's not hungry," replied Tom's mum.
"But he's *always* hungry!" said Tom. "And it's his favourite: marinated chicken chunks in juicy jelly."

The position of the exclamation marks can vary. Here is one possibility:

"Mum!" shouted Tom.
"Now what?" said Tom's mum.
"I know why Dig won't eat his dinner," said Tom.
"It's a new recipe. They've added vegetables! You know he hates vegetables!"

p. 16-17 Clauses and conjunctions

Here are some examples:
1. Dig didn't eat his dinner so Kit ate it instead.
2. Dig and Kit were friends but they were rivals, too.
3. Tom was worried when Dig hadn't eaten his food.
4. Mum wasn't paying attention because she was busy.

1. I put the dog on the lead <u>and</u> we went out for a walk.
2. It felt cold <u>although</u> it was sunny.
3. We played in the park <u>until</u> it was dark.
4. Mum was cross <u>when</u> I got home late.
5. I missed my programme <u>because</u> it came on earlier than usual.

1. I missed the last five minutes of the film. <u>Consequently</u>, I don't know how it ended!
2. I can come to your house. <u>However</u>, I can't stay for long.
3. Firstly, you mix the butter and the sugar. <u>Next</u>, you add the egg.
4. Dad did the shopping. <u>Meanwhile</u>, Mum was at work.
5. Do your homework now. <u>Later</u>, you can go swimming.

p. 18 Relative clauses

There are many possible answers. Here are some suggestions:
The friends<u>, who had known each other for 5 years,</u> decided to meet at the park.
The town<u>, where my dad lived,</u> was difficult to find.

p. 19 Parenthesis (using brackets, dashes and commas)

There are several possible answers. Here are some suggestions:
1. The staircase (735 steps) winds around the inside of the castle.
2. The Himalayas, where the largest mountain in the world is situated, are in Nepal.
3. The weather – thunder and lightning – spoiled our barbecue.
4. The car – annoyingly – would not start when we needed to get to school.

p. 20 Prefix

1. aquarium
   aquatic
   aquamarine
2. vivisect
   vivacious
   vivid
3. geometry
   geology
   geography
4. biography
   bionic
   biological
5. octopus
   octagon
   octave
6. supermarket
   supersonic
   supervisor

p. 21 Suffix

1. instructor
2. actor
3. conductor
4. hopeless
5. sleepless
6. restless
7. excitement
8. movement
9. agreement
10. immediately
11. suddenly
12. extremely

1. spiced
2. caring
3. later
4. biggest
5. swimming
6. stopped

p. 22 Different kinds of writing

Somehow <u>I</u> knew that today was going to be special, even though it started off like every other day – <u>I</u> was going to be late for school again!

To make chocolate brownies <u>you</u> need: flour, cocoa powder, eggs, butter and milk. But first, <u>you</u> need to find an adult to help <u>you</u>!

"I'm so happy!" <u>she</u> said. "I want to thank everyone who voted for me!" <u>They</u> cheered enthusiastically as <u>she</u> lifted the winner's trophy.

p. 26-27 Writing non-fiction

There are many possible answers. Here are some suggestions:
1. The cheetah is fast because it has long legs and an athletic body.
2. The cheetah is faster than the average car.
3. The wildebeest can outrun the cheetah because it can maintain its speed over longer distances.
4. Domestic cats no longer need to chase their dinner.
5. The text is written in present tense.

p. 29 A Recount

1. The following time connectives are used: 'when', 'immediately', 'first', 'then' and 'next' (the box below shows the connectives underlined).

<u>When</u> I arrived home at 7pm, I <u>immediately</u> knew something was wrong. The <u>first</u> thing I noticed was the light through the upstairs window when I knew I hadn't left it on. <u>Then</u> I saw that the front door was wide open! I stepped nervously into the hallway and everything looked okay. <u>Next</u>, I went into the living room and to my dismay I saw that some burglars had broken in! <u>Then</u> I called the police.

2. The text is written in the past tense.
3. The text is written in the first person because the pronouns 'I' and 'my' are used.